GLENCOE

LITERATURE

The Reader's Choice

Literature Groups
Sourcebook

Course 1

Glencoe McGraw-Hill

New York, New York   Columbus, Ohio   Woodland Hills, California   Peoria, Illinois

Glencoe/McGraw-Hill

A Division of The McGraw·Hill Companies

Send all inquiries to:
Glencoe/McGraw-Hill
936 Eastwind Drive
Westerville, Ohio 43081

ISBN 0-02-817308-2

Printed in the United States of America

1 2 3 4 5 6 7 8 9 10 009 03 02 01 00 99

Table of Contents

Table of Contents (continued)

USING LITERATURE GROUPS IN THE CLASSROOM

OVERVIEW

Literature groups are built on the concept of literature circles or discussion groups, which combine independent reading with collaborative work. Students gather into groups and assume specific roles, such as Guide or Geographer, as they discuss a selection from *Glencoe Literature*. Each role should focus on a different aspect of a selection. At this point, assign the Literature Groups activity that appears on the Extending Your Response page in the Student Edition. The role sheets described below will help students familiarize themselves with their roles and carry them out.

By working in literature groups, students can gain a deeper understanding of literature selections, improve their communication skills, and strengthen their ability to work together. The following pages will help you organize, enjoy, and make the most of literature groups in your classroom.

Components

In addition to the guidance provided on the next four pages, this sourcebook includes the following items to support your students as they read and enjoy selections in *Glencoe Literature:*

- **Model Lessons for a Short Selection and a Long Selection** describe two ways to organize Literature Groups. (For more about these two approaches, see "Using the Model Lessons" on page vii.)
- **Nine Discussion Role Sheets** assist students in carrying out the roles in a discussion group. These reproducible sheets explain the roles listed below and provide sample questions. They also encourage students to add their own ideas for exploration within their groups.

Core Roles

Guide: The student in this role directs the group discussions. The Guide makes sure that everyone has an opportunity to share, discussions remain on target, and group members treat each other with respect as they work together.

Highlighter: This student helps group members examine two or three passages from the selection that deserve a closer look. For example, one passage might be puzzling, while another might be disturbing or memorable for some reason.

Sketcher: The Sketcher captures the meaning of a passage or the entire selection in a visual form that can range from a stick-figure cartoon to a charcoal drawing. The emphasis is not on the Sketcher's artistic skills, but on the image or concept he or she shares.

Connector: The student in this role helps group members connect the selection characters or conflict with their own lives or with other curriculum areas, such as social studies, math, science, or art.

Word Master: This student focuses on unfamiliar words or words used in unusual ways. The goal is to help group members not only recognize and understand new words, but also begin to use them in their writing and speaking.

(For information on two more core roles, see the following page for descriptions of the **Genre Master Role Sheets** and **Theme Master Role Sheets**.)

Additional Roles

Investigator: This student researches a topic related to the selection—such as a time period, an event or invention, or a culture—and shares his or her findings with the group.

Librarian: The Librarian may extend the group's study by reviewing additional works by the same author or by identifying other works in *Glencoe Literature* that have the same theme.

Geographer: This student researches and shares information about how the physical and cultural setting affect the selection's characters or conflict.

Summarizer: The Summarizer helps group members recall the content of earlier reading assignments for a particular selection.

- **Eight Genre Master Role Sheets** on blackline masters, listed on page iii, help students with this role lead their groups in analyzing the characteristics of the genres featured at grade six.
- **Eight Theme Master Role Sheets** on blackline masters, listed on page iv, help the Theme Masters guide their group members in applying the theme to the selection they just read, to other selections with the same theme, and to their own lives.
- **Four Additional Poetry Master Role Sheets** on blackline masters, also listed on page iv, focus on specific aspects of poetry to help students better appreciate this genre. **The Genre Master Role Sheet: Poetry** and the four supplementary poetry sheets can be used together. One student might serve as the group's Guide, while the other group members use their own Discussion Role Sheets to contribute to the discussion.
- **Seven Pages of Selection-Specific Suggestions** list many of the selections at this grade level and suggest specific roles to include in the literature groups for those selections. These pages also offer selection-specific writing prompts to encourage students to complete journal entries related to those selections.

SUGGESTIONS FOR GETTING STARTED

Introducing Students to Literature Group Roles: Three Approaches to Consider

- After students read a selection, invite them to carry out three or four of the roles as a class. Distribute those Role Sheets, one at a time, and have the class discuss a few points the person with that role might discuss with a group. Continue this approach with selections from different genres until you have covered all of the roles.
- After students read a selection, divide them into groups of four and give each group a different Role Sheet. Give the groups ten to fifteen minutes to discuss the questions on their Role Sheets, then ask each group to share its insights and conclusions with the class.
- Select several students to model a Literature Group discussion for the class. Assign a different role to each group member (you might take a role yourself), and provide some coaching. Then have the class divide into groups of four or five and assign a different role to each student in each group.

Considering Group Sizes

The less accustomed students are to group work, the smaller your groups should be. After students are familiar with the various roles, organize them into groups of three and assign each group one role. In time, you can increase the group size and have members carry out different roles.

Deciding Which Roles to Assign for Each Selection

You might assign the seven core roles, including Genre Master and Theme Master, for each selection and add the other roles as appropriate. However, a group this size will function well only if students have experience with Literature Groups. To limit group size, assign the roles that are most relevant to a selection and that will help you meet your own goals and objectives for the selection. (The Selection-Specific Suggestions on pages 34–40 can help you choose appropriate roles.) Another approach is to spread the roles among the groups so that all roles are represented, but not in every group. The Guide is the only essential role for each group.

Using the Model Lessons: Two Approaches to Assigning Roles

The model lessons demonstrate two approaches to assigning roles. In the three-day model lesson for a short selection, "The Land of Red Apples," each student in a group is assigned a different role. On Days One and Two, the students carry out their roles within the group. On Day Three, each group draws the name of a role from a container. The student in the group with the role named on the card then carries out the role during the whole-class discussion.

In the four-day model lesson for the longer selection, an excerpt from *When Plague Strikes,* the selection is divided into two reading assignments, and each group is assigned one role. The group members first discuss the selection together, focusing on the group's role. Then one or two group members carry out that role during the class discussion.

Whether you ask individual students or whole groups to carry out a role, you might consider listing the appropriate roles for a selection on the board and allowing the students or groups to choose roles from that list.

Scheduling

The model lessons offer a three-day and a four-day plan for scheduling the Literature Groups based on a class period of fifty minutes. You may need to modify this schedule, depending on the students' familiarity with the Literature Group roles, the length of a selection, your class size, and students' interest in that selection.

Copyright © by The McGraw-Hill Companies, Inc.

Carrying out Your Own Role in the Literature Groups

- **Making Role Assignments:** Make sure that each student carries out as many different roles as possible. A natural leader might enjoy the role of Sketcher, and a quiet student might be an effective Guide in a small-group setting. After students have experienced each role, you might allow them to choose their own roles occasionally, as long as each role you have decided upon for that selection is represented.

- **Providing Individual Help:** After carrying out each role once or twice, students should be able to manage their responsibilities on their own, with some guidance from the Role Sheets. However, you might help the Investigators, Librarians, and Geographers locate appropriate research sources, either providing materials within the classroom or allowing extra time for students to complete these roles.

- **Monitoring Group Discussions:** As students work in groups, move around the room, noting how they are interacting and using their time. Try not to interfere unless you observe a serious violation of classroom rules, and provide guidance only as necessary. For example, you can show students how to disagree without being disagreeable, by saying, "I have another idea," instead of "You're wrong!"

- **Monitoring Class Discussions:** Encourage group members to share responsibility by giving them an opportunity to contribute. You might ask, "Does anyone else in this group have something to add?" Also, make sure each role gets a similar amount of time to share ideas and insights. You might use a timer to divide the time equally, especially during a class presentation.

- **Moving Away from Role Sheets:** In time, students will be able to assume a role without relying on a Role Sheet. Your discussion prompts—such as "What would a Connector ask about this selection?"—will be sufficient to remind students of what they have learned. You might also ask them to make journal entries, writing as a Highlighter, for example.

- **Adding variety:** At the end of a unit, consider having all the students who had a certain role, such as Theme Master, form a panel and share what they have learned about that role. Students enjoy this interaction and tend to bond together as a result of their shared experience. You might set up a different role panel after each unit.

INDIVIDUAL AND GROUP ASSESSMENT

Assessment is an ongoing process that takes many forms. The kinds of questions listed for each role in the Literature Groups model lessons are one way to assess students' grasp of their role responsibilities. Your monitoring of the group and class discussions also allows you to assess whether students are carrying out their roles and working cooperatively. Allow time for self-assessment after group discussions. Ask students to answer questions such as those below. Also, see the inside back cover of this book for a reproducible assessment form.

Myself: What was my role during this group discussion? How well did I carry it out? What was my strength? What could I do better next time?

My group discussion: How well did our group members work together? What was our strength? What could we do better next time?

Our class discussion: How well did we all work together? What was our strength? What could we do better next time?

MODEL LESSONS

Model Lesson for a Short Selection

"The Land of Red Apples" by Zitkala-Ša

Getting Ready

Assignments

Organize the class into six groups. Assign one of these four discussion roles to a student in each group: Guide, Genre Master, Theme Master, and Word Master. Assign the remaining students in each group as Connectors, Highlighters, or Sketchers.

Note: If some groups have only five or six members, ask them to assign a Connector or a Highlighter or a Sketcher. Make sure all three roles are assigned so they can be included in the class presentations on Day Three.

Materials

Give Genre Masters a copy of *Genre Master Role Sheet: Autobiography* and provide Theme Masters with *Theme Master Role Sheet: Where I Belong.* Give copies of the appropriate *Discussion Role Sheets* to students who are completing a role for the first time.

Pre-reading Guidance

As students read "The Land of Red Apples" on pages 55–57, have them consider how they can use their discussion roles to help their group and the entire class better understand the story and appreciate the author's skills.

Day One (50 minutes)

Task Explanation (10 minutes)

Assemble students into their six assigned groups, each with a Guide, Genre Master, Theme Master, and Word Master. Some or all groups may also have a Connector, Highlighter, and/or Sketcher.

Explain that today and on Day Two, students will carry out their roles within their groups. On Day Three, each group will draw a role card from a container. The cards name each role except Guide. The group member with the role named on the card will lead a 5- to 6-minute class discussion or activity on Day Three. Stress that all group members (except Guides) must be ready to share if their role cards are drawn. However, only one member of each group will present his or her role to the class. After the presentations, the Guides will form a panel to share what they learned as they carried out their own roles.

Group Discussions (40 minutes)

To begin, the Guides will use their *Discussion Role Sheets* to help make sure their groups have a general understanding of the selection. Then the Genre Masters will use the *Genre Master Role Sheet: Autobiography* worksheet to help their groups identify the characteristics of autobiographies and to identify the author's purpose in writing this selection. Next, the Theme Masters will invite their group members' input on the theme, following guidelines on the *Theme Master Role Sheet: Where I Belong* worksheet. If time allows, Word Masters will explore the selection's vocabulary. Guides will make sure the group discussions flow smoothly.

Day Two (50 Minutes)

Continued Group Discussions (25 minutes)

The remaining group members will share information with their groups, possibly including the Word Master, Connector, Highlighter, and/or Sketcher.

Group Planning (25 minutes)

Group members will review each role except Guide, focusing on important points to be shared or explored with the class if the group is responsible for that role on Day Three.

Day Three (50 minutes)

Presentation Assignments (5 minutes)

Before class, write all roles except Guide on separate cards and put them in a container. To begin the lesson, have a member of each group draw a card. The group member with the role named on the card will make a short presentation to the class. If no one in the group carried out that role (such as Sketcher), the member will replace that card and draw again.

Class Presentations (35–40 minutes)

A member from each group will lead a short class discussion or activity, sharing insights relating to his or her role. Be prepared to ask each presenter or the class specific questions in order to help students analyze and appreciate the selection. Here are sample questions for "The Land of Red Apples."

> *Genre Master:* How is Zitkala-Ša's description of the children's trip to the boarding school different from the way a "paleface" might have described it?

> *Theme Master:* Do you think Zitkala-Ša eventually felt as if she belonged at the boarding school? Why or why not?

> *Word Master:* In this selection, which of the vocabulary words are used by young people today? Which words could easily become part of a young person's written or spoken vocabulary?

> *Connector:* Do young people ever expect something similar to "a wonderful land of rosy skies"? What are some examples? What tends to happen when our expectations are "sky-high"?

> *Highlighter:* The author writes that she pleaded to go home, but "the ears of the palefaces could not hear me." What did she mean? Why didn't she just write that the adults could not understand the words she was using?

> *Sketcher:* What other drawings did you consider before doing this one? What made you pick this one? How might the author herself have illustrated this story?

Panel Discussion for Guides (5–10 minutes)

Ask the Guides to sit at the front of the room and share what they learned as they carried out their roles. What tips would they give to future Guides about keeping discussions on track or making sure everyone participates?

MODEL LESSONS

Model Lesson for a Longer Selection

from *When Plague Strikes* by James Cross Giblin

Day One (30 minutes)

Getting Ready (20 minutes)

Organize the class into eight groups. Each group will choose one member as its Guide, and the entire group will assume one of these roles: Theme Master, Genre Master, Word Master, Highlighter, Sketcher, Connector, Summarizer, or Geographer. You can assign each group a role or allow the groups to choose their own roles, making sure that all eight roles are chosen.

Note: If your class is small, you might organize seven groups and assign two roles, Highlighter and Connector, to one group.

Materials (5 minutes)

Make sure the Genre Master group has copies of *Genre Master Role Sheet: Expository Nonfiction.* Give the Theme Master group copies of *Theme Master Role Sheet: Getting Through Hard Times.* Provide copies of the appropriate *Discussion Role Sheets* to students who are completing a role for the first time. Make sure they are familiar with their roles and responsibilities.

Assignment (5 minutes)

Ask students to read pages 579–585 of the selection from *When Plague Strikes.* As they read, have them consider how their group can use its role to help classmates better understand the story. Urge students to take notes as they read, perhaps on their *Discussion Role Sheets.*

Day Two (50 minutes)

Task Explanation (5 minutes)

Assemble students into their eight groups, each with a Guide and an assigned role. Explain that today the Guides will help their groups discuss the first part of the reading selection. Then each group will predict what they think may happen next in the selection.

Group Discussions (20 minutes)

Guides will use the suggestions on their *Discussion Role Sheets* to help ensure that group members have a general understanding of the assigned reading. Guides will also help their groups reach a consensus about what will happen next in the selection. Will the plague continue to spread, or will doctors figure out its cause and be able to stop it? Will the Pope survive?

Class Discussion (20 minutes)

Invite a Guide to lead a class discussion about the assigned reading selection. (Or lead the discussion yourself.) Also have groups share their predictions for the rest of the selection. (Try to keep the discussion general and not cover topics that will be covered as the groups carry out their roles on Days Three and Four.)

Assignment (5 minutes)

Have the class read the rest of from *When Plague Strikes,* pages 586–589.

Day Three (50 minutes)

Task Explanation (5 minutes)

Explain that today groups will discuss the last pages of the reading selection. Each group will also plan how to carry out its role in a 5- to 6-minute class presentation today or on Day Four.

Group Discussions and Planning (30 minutes)

The Guides will help their groups discuss the end of the reading selection and check the accuracy of their predictions. Each group will also choose two or three important points to share with the class, related to its assigned role. Group presentations may take a variety of forms, such as discussions, paper-and-pencil activities, and short skits. Encourage groups to involve as many members in their presentations as possible. Those who are not presenting might help by writing questions, gathering information, or preparing visuals, for example.

Class Presentations (15 minutes)

Have the groups take turns making presentations. Begin with the Summarizers, followed by the Genre Masters. Be ready with questions of your own related to *When Plague Strikes,* such as these:

> *Summarizers:* What are some details that you would not include in a summary of this selection? Why?

> *Genre Masters:* Did James Cross Giblin use chronological order, order of importance, or another method to organize this nonfiction selection? How do you know?

Day Four (50 minutes)

Continued Class Presentations (45 minutes)

Ask the remaining groups to make their presentations. Here are more sample questions you might ask:

> *Theme Masters:* What made it so difficult for people living in the fourteenth century to get through those hard times?

> *Word Masters:* In what ways do we use the word *quarantine* today? Why is the word *bubonic* rarely used?

> *Highlighters:* What passages in the story do you think best describe the hopelessness of people living during the plague years?

> *Sketchers:* What illustrations would you add to this selection if you could?

> *Connectors:* Do you think we will ever face an outbreak of the bubonic plague again? Why or why not? Are other plagues occurring now? If so, what are they?

> *Geographers:* Did the plague spread out in all directions from Italy? If not, why?

Wrap-up (5 minutes)

Ask students if they would like to read the rest of *When Plague Strikes.* Discuss what it might describe. Then have students consider the roles they carried out for this selection. Which role would they like to have for the next selection? Why?

Literature Group Activity

Discussion Role Sheet: Guide

Before Reading the Selection
Review this sheet to become familiar with your discussion role responsibilities.

While Reading the Selection
• Jot down questions that you can use to help your group review the selection, such as these:
   – How would you summarize this selection in a sentence or two?
   – Did you enjoy this selection? Why?
   – Did anything in the story surprise you? Make you angry?
   – Is this story believable? Why?
   – Would you like to read other works by this author? Why?
   – Would you like to read more about this subject? Why?
• List some possible discussion questions for this selection:

1. _____

2. _____

3. _____

4. _____

During the Group Discussion
Use the questions you jotted down as you read to help your group review the selection.

• Keep the discussion on track. When members start talking about other topics, remind them of the task at hand. For example, you might say: "The Word Master asked us about this author's choice of words. Which words do you think best describe the main character?"
• Make sure everyone participates in the discussion.
   – If someone is not participating, call on that person by name: "Curt, what do you think the author is telling us?"
   – If someone is dominating the discussion, you might say; "Jona, let's find out what Kelly thinks. Kelly, do you agree or disagree?"
• Model respect for others' opinions.
   – People will be more willing to share their ideas if they know no one will make fun of them. Remember that many questions can have more than one answer.
• Respect others' privacy.
   – Don't insist that all group members share their feelings or experiences if it's clear that some would rather not.
• Keep the group on schedule.
   – For example, point out that the group has only five minutes left to complete a task.

Literature Group Activity

Discussion Role Sheet: Highlighter

Before Reading the Selection
Review this sheet to become familiar with your discussion role responsibilities.

While Reading the Selection
Look for several passages in the selection that are special for some reason. Maybe one is:

puzzling	funny	surprising	disturbing
fascinating	maddening	touching	worth remembering

You might select a passage you disagree with–or one you agree with strongly. You might choose the passage that you think is the most important part of the whole selection, perhaps the turning point of a story. You might select two or three passages for different reasons.

After Reading the Selection
Plan ways for your group to explore these passages, such as these:

- Read the passage aloud and ask the group questions about it.
- Have another student read it aloud and then discuss it as a group.
- Have the group read the passage silently and share their reactions.
- Ask volunteers to act out a scene you have selected.
- Use your imagination to think of other approaches!

Write the passages and your plan below:

1. Page _____ What makes this section special: _____

_____

How I plan to introduce it to the group: _____

Questions I will ask: _____

_____

2. Page _____ What makes this section special: _____

_____

How I plan to introduce it to the group: _____

Questions I will ask: _____

_____

During the Group Discussion
Follow your plan to help group members–or the whole class–appreciate special passages in this selection.

Literature Group Activity

Discussion Role Sheet: Sketcher

Before Reading the Selection
Review this sheet to become familiar with your discussion role responsibilities.

While Reading the Selection
Working alone or with a group of Sketchers, think of images you might create to capture the meaning of a passage in the selection–or the whole selection. For example, you might consider:

drawing a stick-figure cartoon

creating a collage of magazine
    pictures or objects

making a charcoal sketch of one or
    more characters

sketching a scene from the selection

creating a certain texture or
    combination of textures

expressing feelings or actions in the
    selection through colors

The only limits are your imagination and the available time and materials.

After Reading the Selection
• Jot some possibilities below. Add a rough sketch of each one.

• After you've made your choice, create the artwork. Remember: your ideas are more important than your artistic skills!

During the Group Discussion
When it's your turn to share with the group–or with the class, consider these ideas:

• Show your artwork and explain why you selected that image.
• Display your work and invite other group or class members to suggest ways it might relate to the selection. What does it remind them of? What do they think it represents? Whether you tell the group what you actually had in mind is up to you!

Literature Group Activity

Discussion Role Sheet: Connector

Before Reading the Selection
Review this sheet to become familiar with your discussion role responsibilities.

While Reading the Selection
- Think about how the ideas, events, and experiences in the selection apply to young people today. For example, few young people today lead armies into battle, but they do face other kinds of challenges. Few teenagers are suddenly transported back in time, but many have to change schools and leave their friends. Consider the kinds of problems facing the characters. Then ask yourself questions such as those below:
    - Is one character jealous of another one?
    - Does someone feel lonely, worried, or not respected?
    - Is someone desperate to solve a problem or escape a responsibility, no matter what the cost?
    - Did someone make a mistake and then deeply regret it?
    - Is a character trying to prove something to himself, herself, or others?
- Consider what your group has learned in other subject areas about the events or experiences in the selection. Think about social studies, science, math, or health, for example.

After Reading the Selection
Think of ways to help your group or class recognize the connection between their lives and the selection. At the same time, remember not to embarrass anyone who happens to be in a situation similar to one in the selection. Jot your ideas below, along with questions to start a brief discussion.

Page _____   Idea or experience: _____

_____

How it relates to our lives or other subject areas: _____

_____

Questions I will ask: _____

_____

During the Group Discussion
Ask the questions you've selected to help group members see the same connections you did. Encourage others to share their opinions and reactions. Remember that readers often bring different experiences to the same reading selection, so others might see different connections in the reading than you did. The more ideas, the better!

Literature Group Activity

Discussion Role Sheet: Word Master

Before Reading the Selection

Review this sheet to become familiar with your discussion role responsibilities.

While Reading the Selection

Look for words or groups of words that you could discuss with your group or class. These words might be:

surprising	from another language	unfamiliar	touching
critical to the story	repeated to make a point	familiar but used in a new way	related to an interesting occupation

The words you choose do not have to be listed as new vocabulary for the selection. If you're not sure what a word means, look it up in a dictionary. Try to find out the history of the word, too, because that can help explain its meaning and use.

After Reading the Selection

- Think of ways to help your group become comfortable with new words. Your goal is to help group or class members not only remember what the words mean, but also begin to use them in their writing and speaking. You might set up an activity, such as one of these:
  - A paper-and-pencil game, matching words and definitions
  - A twenty-questions game
  - A sentence-writing activity for pairs of students
  - Use your imagination to think of other approaches!
- Write the words you selected below, so you can find them easily:

1. Word _____ What makes this word special: _____

_____

Page _____ How I will help my group learn and use this word: _____

_____

2. Word _____ What makes this word special: _____

_____

Page _____ How I will help my group learn and use this word: _____

_____

During the Group Discussion

Follow your plan to help group members—or the whole class—focus on special words in this selection.

Literature Group Activity

Discussion Role Sheet: Investigator

Before Reading the Selection

Review this sheet to become familiar with your discussion role responsibilities. Your teacher may ask you to focus on a certain topic related to the reading, such as everyday life during the time period when the story takes place. Perhaps you will be asked to gather information about a war or an invention that is important to the story. Maybe your teacher will ask you to find out more about a certain culture. Or you might be invited to choose your own topic to investigate.

While Reading the Selection

Consider how your topic relates to the reading. How does it affect the characters and events in the story? What might the other students in your group or class like to know about this topic?

After Reading the Selection

• Gather information on the topic. You might try one or more of these approaches:
  - Search the Internet.
  - Look in encyclopedias.
  - Interview knowledgeable people.
  - Interview local experts in a certain field.
  - Check other books and magazines.
  - Look in your history, health, or social studies textbooks.
  - Use your imagination to think of other approaches!

List the sources you will check:

_____

_____

• Decide how to share what you have learned. Here are some ways to add interest to your presentation:
  - Gather pictures to display.
  - Play an audio or video recording.
  - Ask other students or parents to help you prepare food from a certain culture.
  - Put on a skit to show everyday life during a certain time period.

Outline your presentation plan:

_____

_____

During the Group Discussion

Follow your plan to help group members—or the whole class—learn more about an interesting aspect of this reading selection.

Literature Group Activity

Discussion Role Sheet: Librarian

Before Reading the Selection

Review this sheet to become familiar with your discussion role responsibilities. Your teacher may ask you to locate or identify other works by the same author or other readings on the same theme. Or you may be instructed to choose which kind of information you gather.

While Reading the Selection

Pay attention to the author or the theme. Summarize the reading so you can compare it to other works by the author or other works with related themes.

After Reading the Selection

• Gather information on the author, including a list of other works. You might try one or more of these approaches:
   – Check your library's card or computer catalog for more works by this author.
   – Look in encyclopedias.
   – Consult reference books, such as literary encyclopedias, which offer the biographies of authors from certain countries or from certain time periods.
   – Search the Internet.
   – Use your imagination to think of other approaches!

Write the sources you will check:

_____

_____

• Locate other books with the same theme. They might be listed on the library catalog under a topic such as "belonging," "identity," or "perspective." Your teacher might help you translate the unit theme into possible topics to check.
• Consider how the works by the same author are similar and different. Or be ready to point out how the works on the same theme are similar to this selection.
• Decide how to share the information. Here are some ways to add interest to your presentation:
   – Display books by the same author–or books on the same theme.
   – Briefly summarize the books you've gathered–or read aloud interesting passages from them.

Outline your presentation plan:

_____

_____

During the Group Discussion

Follow your plan to help group members–or the whole class–locate more selections by the same author or on the same theme.

Literature Group Activity

Discussion Role Sheet: Geographer

Before Reading the Selection

Review this sheet to become familiar with your discussion role responsibilities. Your teacher may ask you to gather information about a specific aspect of the geographic setting in the selection, such as its climate, or you might collect general information about the location.

While Reading the Selection

Take notes on the location or locations mentioned in the selection. Notice how they influence the characters or events in the selection. For example, consider why the author wrote about a nonfiction event that took place in this location—or why the author purposely chose this place for a fictional story.

After Reading the Selection

- Gather information about the location (or locations), the people who live there, the climate, the physical features of the setting (such as mountains or rivers), and any other data that may interest your classmates. You might try one or more of these approaches:
    - Consult an atlas, map, or globe.
    - Look in encyclopedias (printed books or compact discs).
    - Check a social studies or geography textbook.
    - Search the Internet, using keywords.
    - Use your imagination to think of other ways to gather this information.

List the sources you will check:

_____

_____

- Decide how to share the information. Your goal is to explain the role of the location in the reading selection. Here are some ways to add interest to your presentation:
- Display a large map with the setting of the selection marked or outlined in some way. You might trace a character's travels with yarn or colored markers.
- Locate and offer books about the specific setting or the country or region in which it is located.

Outline your presentation plan, along with points you want to make:

_____

_____

During the Group Discussion

Follow your plan to help group members—or the whole class—learn more about the selection's geographic setting.

Literature Group Activity

Discussion Role Sheet: Summarizer

Before Reading the Selection
Review this sheet to become familiar with your discussion role responsibilities.

While Reading the Selection
Outline the selection below, jotting down the main events. Also list some details at this point.
You can always eliminate them from your summary later.

_____

_____

_____

_____

_____

After Reading the Selection
• Review your points and choose three to five that describe the main events and ideas in the
  selection. (What seemed like a key point while you read may not seem so important now. Or you
  may know now that what you thought was a detail is actually an important incident in the story.)
• Write a summary of the selection. Use complete sentences.

_____

_____

_____

_____

_____

• If possible, read your summary to a group member. Ask if he or she thinks you have covered the
  main points. If not, what should you add or delete from the summary?

During the Group Discussion
As you read your summary to the group or class, try to maintain eye contact with your listeners.
You might ask if anyone would add anything to the summary, especially if you did not have the
opportunity to read it to a group member ahead of time.

Literature Group Activity

Genre Master Role Sheet: Autobiography

Before Reading the Selection

Review the elements of an autobiography (listed below) and tips for reading autobiography on pages 60–63 of your textbook.

While Reading the Selection

Notice how the author uses the seven elements. Jot down two or three you want to explore with your group.

_____

During the Group Discussion

Lead a discussion or a quick activity relating to some or all of the seven elements. Below are some examples:

• **Point of View:** Have the group select a part of the selection written from the subject's point of view and restate it from the point of view of someone else in that situation.

_____

• **A Story:** Help group members agree on the beginning, middle, and end of the event.

_____

• **Chronological Order:** Ask the group to name the important events in the narrative and then put them in order.

_____

• **Author's Purpose:** Discuss why the author wrote about his or her life. What did the author want to share or explain?

_____

• **Details:** Look for the details the author chose to include, such as bits of conversation, feelings, descriptions of places, or even a certain look or gesture from an important person in his or her life.

_____

• **One Interpretation:** Discuss a different interpretation of part of the event.

_____

• **The Personal Made Public:** Explore times when someone might have feelings similar to those the author describes.

Literature Group Activity

Genre Master Role Sheet: Poetry

Before Reading the Selection

Review the elements and forms of poetry and tips for reading poetry on pages 176–179 of your textbook.

While Reading the Selection

Decide what form this poem takes. Is it narrative or lyric? Does it use regular rhythm, or is it free verse? Write down which of the bulleted elements listed below appear in this poem.

_____

During the Group Discussion

Here are some ideas to help your group identify and appreciate the elements in this poem.

• **Rhythm and Rhyme:** Challenge the members of your group to determine if the poem uses regular rhythm. If it does, have them clap out the rhythm of the poem as they say it aloud. Invite them to identify any pairs of words that rhyme.

_____

• **Onomatopoeia** is the use of words that imitate or suggest the sound being described. Ask if anyone can find words in the poem that imitate sounds, including sounds animals make. Point out that these terms can be as familiar as the word *whisper.*

_____

• **Repetition:** Have members of your group find examples of repeated sounds, words, or phrases. Remind them that repeated sounds can occur at the end of words, as well as the beginning.

_____

• **Imagery:** Describe an image that is suggested by the poem. Invite other students to share what they "saw" as they read.

_____

• **Figures of Speech** are unusual or unexpected comparisons between one thing and something else that is more familiar. Challenge your group to point out times when the poet compares things, perhaps using **similes** or **metaphors.**

_____

• **Personification** is a figure of speech in which a human quality is given to an animal, object, or idea. Does the poet make an animal or an object seem human? How does that help get the poet's point across?

_____

Literature Group Activity

Genre Master Role Sheet: Biography

Before Reading the Selection

Review the four elements of a biography (listed below) and tips for reading biographies on pages 266–267 of your textbook.

While Reading the Selection

Notice how the author uses the four elements. Write down which ones you want to explore with your group.

_____

During the Group Discussion

Lead a discussion or a quick activity relating to some or all of the four elements. Here are some ideas to help you get started. Jot notes below to help you remember what you planned.

• **Facts:** Have volunteers point out some facts the author incorporated into the selection. Discuss where or how the author might have gathered these facts. Did the author live at the same time as the subject of the biography? If not, where would these facts have been available?

_____

• **Characters:** Discuss why the author might have chosen this person to write about. Did the author share something with the person, such as a culture or a physical limitation? What other interesting characters are included in the biography?

_____

• **Setting:** Ask the members of your group how they think the setting or settings of the subject's life influenced him or her. Would the subject's life have turned out differently if he or she grew up in another region or during another time period? How did major events during that time period, such as a war or the struggle for civil rights, affect the subject of this selection?

_____

• **Generalizations:** Challenge your group to point out generalizations that the author made about the subject of this biography. For example, did the author seem to think that the subject was brave–or lucky? courageous–or stubborn? What incidents does the author include to support these generalizations? How could readers determine whether the generalizations are accurate? (by reading other biographies about the same person)

_____

Literature Group Activity

Genre Master Role Sheet: Short Story

Before Reading the Selection

Review the five elements of a short story (listed below) and tips for reading short stories on pages 350–353 of your textbook.

While Reading the Selection

Notice how the author uses the five elements and constructs the plot. Write down which elements you want to explore with your group.

_____

During the Group Discussion

Lead a discussion or quick activity relating to some or all of the elements. Here are some ideas to help you get started. Jot down notes to help you remember your plan.

- **Setting:** Ask group members how they think the setting (or settings) of the story influences its events. Do the beliefs or values of a town or a time period play an important role? Could this story take place anywhere, anytime? Why or why not?

_____

- **Characters:** Have the students in your group identify the protagonist, or main character, in the story. Are his or her actions and thoughts believable? Are they supposed to be? Is it easy to tell the characters apart by their actions or dialogue?

_____

- **Point of View:** Discuss the story's point of view. Is it told by the main character in first person? Or by an unseen narrator in the third-person? How would the story change if it were told from another character's point of view?

_____

- **Theme:** Invite volunteers to suggest possible themes for this selection. Remember that readers may come to different conclusions about a theme—or state the same theme in different words. Discuss how the story theme relates to the theme for this unit.

_____

- **Plot:** Help your group pinpoint the main conflict in this short story, the rising action as things get worse, the climax or high point, the falling action in response to the climax, and the final resolution.

_____

Literature Group Activity

Genre Master Role Sheet: Folktale

Before Reading the Selection

Review the four elements of a folktale (listed below) and tips for reading folktales on pages 442–445 of your textbook. Decide whether this selection would be considered a folktale (a story passed down through the generations), a trickster tale (in which one character tries to fool another one), or a fairy tale (a story with magical characters in it).

While Reading the Selection

Notice how the author uses the four elements. Make some notes below about which ones you want to explore with your group.

_____

During the Group Discussion

Lead a discussion or a quick activity relating to some or all of the elements. Here are some ideas to help you get started. Jot down notes to help you remember your plan.

- **Setting:** Ask group members if the setting of this folktale reminds them of a certain city or region. Why do they think folktale authors often invent imaginative settings?

_____

- **Characters:** Discuss whether the characters in folktales seem more real than the settings of these stories. What makes them seem real, even when they are trolls or other creatures? (The characters usually have human emotions, including anger, jealousy, and greed. We can identify with them!)

_____

- **Magic:** Ask your group whether there is magic in this folktale—or maybe just exaggeration. Why do many readers enjoy stories with magic in them? (Perhaps many of us would like to believe there is a magic solution for our problems.)

_____

- **Moral:** Explore the lesson in this story with your group. Are readers supposed to learn something from this tale? What behaviors does it warn against? What terrible things are likely to happen if readers ignore the lesson in this tale? What are some other folktales that teach a similar lesson?

_____

Literature Group Activity

Genre Master Role Sheet: Expository Nonfiction

Before Reading the Selection

Review the elements of nonfiction writing (listed below) and reading tips on pages 560–563 of your textbook.

While Reading the Selection

Notice how the author uses the elements. Write down the elements you want to explore with your group.

_____

During the Group Discussion

Lead a discussion or quick activity relating to some or all of the elements. Here are some ideas to help you get started. Jot down notes to help you remember your plan.

• **Topic and Purpose:** Ask group members to locate sentences that explain the selection's purpose and topic. Where do these sentences occur in the selection? Help the group compare this type of organization with that of a newspaper article.

_____

• **Chronological or Logical Order:** Discuss whether the article moves forward chronologically—or sometimes moves back in time or even jumps ahead. Why has the author presented information in this order? Is any information presented in order of importance, instead of chronologically?

_____

• **Subheads:** Have volunteers read aloud the subheads in the selection. Discuss their function. Would students in your group rather read the selection without subheads? Why or why not?

_____

• **Background Facts:** Invite volunteers to identify some of the facts that the author weaves into the reporting of events. Ask which of these facts could be safely omitted. Which ones are essential to the story?

_____

• **Definitions of Terms:** Point out examples of unfamiliar terms that are defined during the story or in a glossary at the end. Ask students if they think the author should have defined any additional terms.

Literature Group Activity

Genre Master Role Sheet: Drama

Before Reading the Selection

Review the four elements of a drama (listed below) and reading tips on pages 662–665 of your textbook.

While Reading the Selection

Notice how the author uses the four elements. Make some notes below about which ones you want to explore with your group.

_____

_____

During the Group Discussion

Lead a discussion or quick activity relating to some or all of the elements. Here are some examples to help you get started. Jot down notes to help you remember your plan.

- **Script:** Have the students in your group compare the script with a story written in paragraph form. How are they similar and different? Which is easier to follow? Which leaves more to the reader's imagination?

_____

_____

- **Narrator:** Discuss whether this reading selection has a narrator or narrators. If so, what role do they have in the play? That is, is the narrator a character or a group of characters, such as a chorus? Or does the narrator stay off-stage? What parts of the story does the narrator help tell?

_____

_____

- **Dialogue:** Ask your group whether they think they could identify a character in the play just by reading his or her dialogue. How does the author change the dialogue for each character? How much of the story is told through dialogue?

_____

_____

- **Stage Directions:** Explore how stage directions help readers visualize the action. How is this same action expressed in a short story? Are any of the stage directions distracting?

_____

_____

Literature Group Activity

Genre Master Role Sheet: Science Fiction

Before Reading the Selection

Review the four elements of science fiction (listed below) and reading tips on pages 768–769 of your textbook.

While Reading the Selection

Notice how the author uses the four elements. Make some notes below about which ones you want to explore with your group.

_____

During the Group Discussion

Lead a discussion or quick activity relating to some or all of the elements. Here are some examples to help you get started. Jot down notes to help you remember your plan.

- **Setting:** Have the students in your group analyze the setting of this story. Does the action take place on another planet–or is the setting familiar and comfortable, until something very unusual happens? Does science fiction have to take place in a strange setting to be interesting? Why or why not?

_____

- **Scientific Basis:** Challenge your group members to list some rules of science that control or affect what happens in this selection. For example, maybe the characters are able to do certain things, but not others. What are some scientific principles that control our lives? (One example: most people can walk, but people can't fly.)

_____

- **Plot:** Discuss how the conflict of the plot depends on the setting and the "rules" that control what happens–or can happen–in the story. Could this plot occur in an everyday setting on Earth? Why or why not?

_____

- **Theme:** Explore what this selection says about our everyday lives. Does it warn us to change our ways, or will we face a catastrophe in the future? What comments is the author making about our priorities and values? How does the theme of the selection relate to the theme of this unit?

_____

Literature Group Activity

Theme Master Role Sheet: Where I Belong

Before Reading the Selection

Review the information about this theme on page 2 of your textbook. Also review the other selections in this theme that you have read so far. Think about how these selections relate to the theme "Where I Belong." Write your conclusions below.

_____

_____

_____

While Reading the Selection

Jot down questions you can ask to help your group better understand the theme. The examples below will get you started, but be sure to add questions of your own that relate to the selection you are reading.

- Think about the other selections you have read with the theme of "Where I Belong." How are the characters' experiences similar? How are they different?
- Why do you think this selection was included in this theme?
- In this selection, how do other people's actions affect whether the main character feels he or she belongs?
- How do the main character's own thoughts and actions affect whether he or she fits into this new setting?

Add your own questions:

_____

_____

_____

_____

During the Group Discussion

Ask the questions you prepared. You might also discuss the points below to help group members apply the theme to their own lives. Remember to respect others' opinions about how the theme relates to this selection and to people in general.

- What are some things that make us feel as if we belong some place? As if we don't belong?
- How can we help others feel that they belong at school or in our neighborhoods or our community?

Literature Group Activity

Theme Master Role Sheet: Through Other Eyes

Before Reading the Selection

Review the information about this theme on page 114 of your textbook. Also review the other selections in this theme that you have read so far. Think about how these selections relate to the theme "Through Other Eyes." Write your conclusions below.

_____

_____

_____

While Reading the Selection

Jot down questions you can ask to help your group better understand the theme. The examples below will get you started, but be sure to add questions of your own that relate to the selection you are reading.

- Think about the other selections you have read with the theme of "Through Other Eyes." Whose viewpoint are readers being encouraged to appreciate? That is, whose eyes are we supposed to look through?
- Why do you think this selection was included in this theme?
- In this selection, whose eyes do we look through? What do we see that we don't ordinarily see— or even think about? Does what you see surprise you? Why or why not?
- How is the main character's point of view similar to a human point of view? How is it different?

Add your own questions:

_____

_____

_____

_____

During the Group Discussion

Ask the questions you prepared. You might also discuss the points below to help group members apply the theme to their lives. Remember to respect others' opinions about how the theme relates to this selection and to people in general.

- In what situations might people try to understand an animal's point of view?
- In what situations do we try to understand another person's point of view? What often happens when we don't try?
- How do you feel when others understand your point of view? How do you feel when they don't? How can you help others understand your viewpoint? How can you better understand theirs?

Literature Group Activity

Theme Master Role Sheet: Growing Times

Before Reading the Selection

Review the information about this theme on page 214 of your textbook. Also review the other selections in this theme that you have read so far. Think about how these selections relate to the theme "Growing Times." Write your conclusions below.

_____

_____

_____

While Reading the Selection

Jot down questions you can ask to help your group better understand the theme. The examples below will get you started, but be sure to add questions of your own that relate to the selection you are reading.

• Think about the other selections you have read with the theme of "Growing Times." Are all the main characters facing the same ups and downs as they grow up? How are their experiences similar? How are they different?
• Why do you think this selection was included in this theme?
• In this selection, how old is the main character? Does he or she want to grow up? Why or why not? What does this character seem to be telling himself or herself about growing up?
• Is the main character making the best of these "growing times"? Or is he or she doing something to make growing up more difficult? Explain.

Add your own questions:

_____

_____

_____

_____

During the Group Discussion

Ask the questions you prepared. You might also discuss the points below to help group members apply the theme to their lives. Remember to respect others' opinions about how the theme relates to this selection and to people in general.

• Which years of growing up do you think will be the most fun? Which years might be the hardest? Why?
• Growing up means more than getting older. How can you tell whether someone is "growing up"?
• Is growing up the same for everyone everywhere? Explain.

Literature Group Activity

Theme Master Role Sheet: What's Most Important

Before Reading the Selection

Review the information about this theme on page 308 of your textbook. Also review the other selections in this theme that you have read so far. Think about how these selections relate to the theme "What's Most Important." Write your conclusions below.

_____

_____

_____

While Reading the Selection

Jot down questions you can ask to help your group better understand the theme. The examples below will get you started, but be sure to add questions of your own that relate to the selection you are reading.

- Think about the other selections you have read with the theme "What's Most Important." What kinds of things did the main characters discover were most important? Not so important?
- Why do you think this selection was included in this theme?
- At the beginning of this selection, what does the main character think is really important? How does this affect his or her decisions, actions, and relationships with others?
- Does the character change his or her mind about what's most important? If so, what causes this change of mind, and is it believable? Explain.

  Add your own questions:

_____

_____

_____

_____

During the Group Discussion

Ask the questions you prepared. You might also discuss the points below to help group members apply the theme to their lives. Be sure to respect others' opinions about how the theme relates to this selection and to people in general.

- What are some ways that people decide—or discover—what's most important?
- How can you tell what's most important to someone?
- In deciding whether to follow someone's advice, should you consider what's most important to this person? Why or why not?
- Do you think people usually change their minds about what's important as they grow older?

Literature Group Activity

Theme Master Role Sheet: The Will to Win

Before Reading the Selection

Review the information about this theme on page 406 of your textbook. Also review the other selections in this theme that you have read so far. Think about how these selections relate to the theme "The Will to Win." Write your conclusions below.

_____

_____

_____

While Reading the Selection

Jot down questions you can ask to help your group better understand the theme. The examples below will get you started, but be sure to add questions of your own that relate to the selection you are reading.

• Think about the other selections you have read with the theme "The Will to Win." What did the characters want to win? Does winning always mean competing against other people? Explain.
• Why do you think this selection was included in this theme?
• In this selection, what obstacles nearly prevent the main character from winning? What do many people do when faced these kinds of obstacles?
• What helps the character in this selection gain or strengthen a will to win? Does the character succeed mostly because of inner determination or mostly because of pressure from others? Explain.

   Add your own questions:

_____

_____

_____

_____

During the Group Discussion

Ask the questions you prepared. You might also discuss the points below to help group members apply the theme to their lives. Remember to respect others' opinions about how the theme relates to this selection and to people in general.

• Can someone give you a will to win? Why or why not?
• Do you think a person must have a will to win in order to be happy? Explain.
• When might a will to win lead to trouble?

Literature Group Activity

Theme Master Role Sheet: Getting Through Hard Times

Before Reading the Selection

Review the information about this theme on page 492 of your textbook. Also review the other selections in this theme that you have read so far. Think about how these selections relate to the theme "Getting Through Hard Times." Write your conclusions below.

_____

_____

_____

While Reading the Selection

Jot down questions you can ask to help your group better understand the theme. The examples below will get you started, but be sure to add questions of your own that relate to the selection you are reading.

- Think about the other selections you have read with the theme of "Getting Through Hard Times." What did the experiences have in common? What helped the characters face challenges?
- Why do you think this selection was included in this theme?
- In this selection, do the main character (or characters) expect hard times? What is their first reaction to them? What personal traits help them succeed in the end?
- What do the characters learn about themselves, other people, or life in general as a result of getting through hard times?

    Add your own questions:

_____

_____

_____

_____

During the Group Discussion

Ask the questions you prepared. You might also discuss the points below to help group members apply the theme to their lives. Remember to respect others' opinions about how the theme relates to this selection and to people in general.

- What kinds of "hard times" do people sometimes cause for themselves? What kinds of hard times are the result of forces outside their control?
- What are some things that help determine how each person faces hard times?
- How might our definition of "hard times" change from one place to another or from one time period to another?

Literature Group Activity

Theme Master Role Sheet: Old Tales, New Twists

Before Reading the Selection

Review the information about this theme on page 604 of your textbook. Also review the other selections in this theme that you have read so far. Think about how these selections relate to the theme "Old Tales, New Twists." Write your conclusions below.

_____

_____

_____

While Reading the Selection

Jot down questions you can ask to help your group better understand the theme. The examples below will get you started, but be sure to add questions of your own that relate to the selection you are reading.

- Think about the other selections you have read with the theme of "Old Tales, New Twists." Which of these stories have you heard before? Why do you think people have been telling these stories for generations? Do you think people will ever stop telling them?
- Why do you think this selection was included in this theme?
- In this selection, what "lesson" does the author want readers to understand? Does this lesson apply in our modern world? Why or why not?
- How do you think the cultural background of this story influences its characters and the events in it, including the ending?

Add your own questions:

_____

_____

_____

_____

During the Group Discussion

Ask the questions you prepared. You might further explore the theme by discussing the points below. Remember to respect others' opinions about how the theme relates to this selection and to people in general.

- Do people still like to hear stories in which at least some of the characters are talking animals? Do any popular recent movies, television shows, or videos include talking animals? Which ones?
- In what ways (if any) are urban legends, such as stories about alligators living in the sewer systems, modern versions of old tales?

Literature Group Activity

Theme Master Role Sheet: To Strange Places

Before Reading the Selection

Review the information about this theme on page 690 in your textbook. Also review the other selections in this theme that you have read so far. Think about how these selections relate to the theme "To Strange Places." Write your conclusions below.

_____

_____

_____

While Reading the Selection

Jot down questions you can ask to help your group better understand the theme. The examples below will get you started, but be sure to add questions of your own that relate to the selection you are reading.

- Think about the other selections you have read with the theme of "To Strange Places." What are some of the strange places the stories have taken us to? What did you like about these trips? Was there anything you did not like about one or more of them?
- Why do you think this selection was included in this theme?
- In this selection, is it the setting, the time period, the characters, the events, or something else that makes the story unusual? What parts of the story seem believable and real?
- How does the author encourage you to use your imagination in this story? What things happen to let you know you are in a "strange place"?

  Add your own questions:

_____

_____

_____

_____

During the Group Discussion

Ask the questions you prepared. You might further explore the theme by discussing the points below. Remember to respect others' opinions about how the theme relates to this selection and to people in general.

- What are some things that make a place "strange"? What changes might make your own neighborhood strange?
- Why do you think some authors place their stories in strange settings? Why do many readers enjoy stories in this kind of setting?

Literature Group Activity

Discussion Role Sheet: Poetry Master—Types of Poetry

Before Reading the Selection
Review this sheet to become familiar with your discussion role and the types of poetry.

While Reading the Selection
Decide whether this selection is a narrative, lyric, or free verse poem.

After Reading the Selection
Think of ways to help your group understand the three different types of poetry described below:

• **Narrative poetry:** These poems tell a story. Some are serious. Others, such as "The Walrus and the Carpenter" on page 707, are meant to be fun.

To help your group, identify narrative poetry, ask:

1. Does this poem tell a story? If so, what is the plot—the conflict, rising action, climax, and so on?
2. Who are the characters in the story?

Add your own questions:

_____

• **Lyric poetry:** Lyric poems express thoughts and feelings or describe scenes. They are often short, such as "The Shark" on page 186. The words to songs are forms of lyric poetry.

Ask your group:

1. Does this poem tell a story or does it describe something? How do you know?
2. What feeling or picture does this poem bring to your mind?

Add your own questions:

_____

• **Free verse:** These poems express a feeling or an idea. Free verse usually does not rhyme and has lines of different lengths. "April Rain Song" on page 325 is written in free verse.

Ask your group:

1. Do any of the lines rhyme? Are any lines of the same length?
2. What picture does the poem bring to your mind?

Add your own questions:

_____

During the Group Discussion
Ask questions to help your group members identify each type of poem they read.

Literature Group Activity

Discussion Role Sheet: Poetry Master—Rhyming Patterns

Before Reading the Selection

Review this sheet to become familiar with your discussion role responsibilities and with rhyming patterns.

While Reading the Selection

Decide whether this selection uses a one-, two-, or three-syllable rhyming pattern—or a combination of them.

After Reading the Selection

Think of ways to help your group recognize the rhyming patterns described below:

- **One-syllable rhyming:** This pattern uses one-syllable words that end with the same vowel sound or vowel-consonant combination. The words cry and die in "Whatif" on page 495 are an example of one-syllable rhyming. Another example is in "The Walrus and the Carpenter" on page 707, which uses the words *might, bright,* and *night.*

  Write examples of one-syllable rhyming here:

  _____

  _____

- **Two-syllable rhyming:** The words in this pattern have two or more syllables that rhyme. For example, "The Shark" on page 186 uses *grabber* and *drabber.* In "The Pied Piper of Hamelin," examples on page 697 include *grumbling, rumbling,* and *tumbling.*

  Write examples of two-syllable rhyming here:

  _____

  _____

- **Three-syllable rhyming:** The words in this pattern have three or more syllables that rhyme. In "The Pied Piper of Hamelin," examples on page 700 include *clattering, chattering,* and *scattering.*

  Write examples of three-syllable rhyming below. (They are more difficult to find!)

  _____

  _____

During the Group Discussion

Use the information above to help your group members identify rhyming patterns.

$\mathcal{L}$iterature $\mathcal{G}$roup $\mathcal{A}$ctivity

Discussion Role Sheet: Poetry Master—Repetition

Before Reading the Selection
Review this sheet to become familiar with your discussion role responsibilities and with repetition patterns.

While Reading the Selection
Look for examples of the repetition of beginning sounds or words, phrases, or sentences.

After Reading the Selection
Think of ways to help your group recognize the repetition patterns described below:

- **Repetition of beginning sounds (alliteration):** Alliteration is the repetition of sounds at the beginning of words. Poets use alliteration to shape the way their poems sound and to emphasize certain words. "The Bat" on page 199 uses alliteration:
  "He likes the attic of an aging house."
  "His fingers make a hat about his head."
  "When mice with wings can wear a human face."

  Write examples of alliteration here:

  _____

- **Repetition of words:** Poets often repeat words to emphasize ideas and to help tie the parts of a poem together. In "Whatif" on page 495, Shel Silverstein begins nearly every line with the title of the poem with "Whatif." In "The Shark" on page 186, the poet repeats the word *thought* many times to focus readers' attention on the shark's dark, although simple, nature.

  Write examples of word repetition here:

  _____

- **Repetition of phrases or sentences:** Like the chorus of a song, poems often repeat phrases and sentences to stress the ideas in them. For example, in "Life Doesn't Frighten Me" on page 496, Maya Angelou repeats the title at the end of each stanza. She varies this sentence just a little each time and adds "at all."

  Write more examples of the repetition of phrases and sentences here.

  _____

During the Group Discussion
Use the information above to help your group members locate and identify examples of repetition.

Literature Group Activity

Discussion Role Sheet: Poetry Master–Similes and Metaphors

Before Reading the Selection

Review this sheet to become familiar with your discussion role responsibilities, along with similes and metaphors.

While Reading the Selection

Look for similes and metaphors to use as examples.

After Reading the Selection

Think of ways to help your group recognize similes and metaphors, described below:

- **Similes:** A simile points out how two unlike things are alike in some way. It uses the words *like* or *as*. For example, in "Ankylosaurus" on page 185, Jack Prelutsky says that this dinosaur "was built *like* a tank." Its hide was "*as* sturdy *as* steel."

  Not only poets use similes. Authors in all genres use them to paint pictures in readers' minds. Tell your group that sentences containing the words *like* or *as* do not automatically contain similes. For example, consider this sentence: "Craig is as friendly as Julianne." This is not a simile because the two things being compared–two people–are very similar. To be a simile, the sentence might read: "Craig is as friendly as a lost puppy."

  Ask your group to find similes–in this poem, in other poems, or in other selections–and identify the two things being compared. Discuss why the authors used those similes, such as to help describe a character or scene, add humor, or create a mood.

  Jot down your own questions and examples to discuss with your group:

  _____

  _____

- **Metaphors:** A metaphor is a comparison that does not use the words *like* or *as*. It says that one thing *is* something else. One example is in the poem "To Young Readers" on page 33. The poet writes that "Good books are good nutrition," meaning that books can nourish us.

  Like similes, metaphors are found in all types of writing. Challenge your group to identify several metaphors and explain what they mean.

  Write down your own questions and examples to discuss with your group:

  _____

  _____

During the Group Discussion

Ask questions to help your group members identify similes and metaphors.

Selection-Specific Suggestions

The suggestions below will help you select Literature Group roles for most of the selections at this grade level.

The Guide and three other recommended roles are listed for each selection. For example, "The Circuit" is the first selection in its theme unit, so the Theme Master is listed. Being able to draw a connection to students' experience will make the selection more interesting, so Connector is suggested. An understanding of the geographic setting will also be important so Geographer is assigned. Four more roles are also suggested for you to consider assigning.

This section also offers discussion/writing prompts for most selections. You might write them on the board as prompts for journal entries, or you could use them as the final discussion question for that selection.

Theme 1: Where I Belong

"The Circuit," pages 5–11
Recommended roles: Guide, Theme Master, Connector, Geographer
Also suggested: Highlighter, Sketcher, Word Master, Investigator
Writing Prompt: "How might Panchito respond if a teacher tries to help him at his next school?"

from *Little by Little,* pages 17–26
Recommended roles: Guide, Theme Master, Genre Master, Connector
Also suggested: Highlighter, Sketcher, Librarian, Geographer
Writing Prompt: "How did books help Jean Little feel comfortable–help her belong–in more places?"

"To Young Readers," page 33
"Arithmetic," page 34
Recommended roles: Guide, Highlighter, Connector, Poetry Master for Similes and Metaphors
Also suggested: Sketcher, Word Master, Librarian, Poetry Master for Types of Poetry
Writing Prompt: "Which school subject is your favorite? Why?"

"The All-American Slurp," pages 40–48
Recommended roles: Guide, Theme Master, Highlighter, Connector
Also suggested: Genre Master, Sketcher, Word Master, Geographer
Writing Prompt: "Why do you think different cultures have developed different table manners?"

"The Land of Red Apples," pages 55–57
Recommended roles: Guide, Theme Master, Genre Master, Word Master
Also suggested: Highlighter, Sketcher, Connector, Geographer
Writing Prompt: "During the late 1800s, how do you think children from the East would have reacted if they had been sent on a train to live with Native American families?"

"Primary Lessons," pages 65–72
Recommended roles: Guide, Theme Master, Genre Master, Geographer
Also suggested: Highlighter, Sketcher, Connector, Word Master
Writing Prompt: "Why do you think this author chose to write about her first day at school?"

from *The Lost Garden,* pages 77–82
Recommended roles: Guide, Genre Master, Theme Master, Word Master
Also suggested: Highlighter, Sketcher, Connector, Investigator
Writing Prompt: "What kinds of things did Laurence Yep learn from his grandmother, even though he could not talk with her?"

from *Homesick*, pages 87–99
Recommended roles: Guide, Sketcher, Connector, Geographer
Also suggested: Genre Master, Theme Master, Highlighter, Investigator
Writing Prompt: "Do you think Jean Fritz ever became homesick for China? Why or why not?"

Theme 2: Through Other Eyes

from *Brother Wolf*, pages 117–118
"Why Dogs Are Tame," pages 119–122
Recommended roles: Guide, Theme Master, Highlighter, Sketcher
Also suggested: Genre Master, Connector, Word Master, Investigator
Writing Prompt: "Can we ever really see the world through an animal's eyes? Explain.

"Mowgli's Brothers," pages 128–145
Recommended roles: Guide, Theme Master, Connector, Word Master
Also suggested: Genre Master, Highlighter, Geographer, Summarizer
Writing Prompt: "Do you think Mowgli will return to the jungle to meet with his wolf family again? Why or why not?"

"The Boy Who Lived with the Bears," pages 149–153
Recommended roles: Guide, Genre Master, Connector, Word Master
Also suggested: Theme Master, Highlighter, Sketcher, Librarian
Writing Prompt: "Which kind of forest animal would you live with, if you had a choice? Why?"

"Koko: Smart Signing Gorilla," pages 159–162
Recommended roles: Guide, Theme Master, Sketcher, Word Master
Also suggested: Genre Master, Highlighter, Connector, Investigator
Writing Prompt: "What could we learn from an animal that could talk?"

"Zlateh the Goat," pages 167–172
Recommended roles: Guide, Highlighter, Sketcher, Connector
Also suggested: Genre Master, Theme Master, Word Master, Librarian
Writing Prompt: "Do you think Aaron reads too much into Zlateh's bleating? Why or why not?"

"The Naming of Cats," pages 181–182
Recommended roles: Guide, Genre Master, Word Master, Poetry Master for Repetition
Also suggested: Theme Master, Sketcher, Connector, Librarian
Writing Prompt: "What would you name yourself, if you could choose a new name? Why?"

"Ankylosaurus," page 185
"The Shark," page 186
Recommended roles: Guide, Sketcher, Poetry Master for Similes and Metaphors, Poetry Master for Rhyming Patterns
Also suggested: Genre Master, Theme Master, Word Master, Investigator
Writing Prompt: "If you could read more poems by one of these authors, which author would you choose? Why?"

"Dinner Together," page 193
"How soft a Caterpillar steps–," page 194
Recommended roles: Guide, Genre Master, Sketcher, Poetry Master for Types of Poetry
Also suggested: Theme Master, Connector, Word Master, Investigator
Writing Prompt: "What might a spider or a caterpillar say to us, if it could talk?"

"The Bat," page 199
"A Minor Bird," page 200
Recommended roles: Guide, Genre Master, Sketcher, Poetry Master for Rhyming Patterns
Also suggested: Theme Master, Highlighter, Connector, Investigator
Writing Prompt: "Write a poem about people from the point of view of a bat or a bird."

Theme 3: Growing Times

"La Bamba," pages 217–224
Recommended roles: Guide, Theme Master, Connector, Word Master
Also suggested: Genre Master, Highlighter, Sketcher, Librarian
Writing Prompt: "Describe something you volunteered to do that turned out differently than you expected."

"Shoes for Hector," pages 231–235
Recommended roles: Guide, Theme Master, Connector, Word Master
Also suggested: Genre Master, Highlighter, Sketcher, Librarian
Writing Prompt: "Hector is worried what his friends will think of his shoes. Do you ever worry about what your friends think? Explain."

"Eleven," pages 239–242
Recommended roles: Guide, Theme Master, Sketcher, Connector
Also suggested: Genre Master, Highlighter, Word Master, Librarian
Writing Prompt: "Do you agree that when you're eleven, you're also ten, nine, eight, and all the other younger ages? Why?"

"The Sidewalk Racer or On the Skateboard," page 247
"Day Dreamers," pages 248–249
Recommended roles: Guide, Genre Master, Word Master, Poetry Master for Rhyming Patterns
Also suggested: Theme Master, Sketcher, Connector, Poetry Master for Similes and Metaphors
Writing Prompt: "Explain when you do your best daydreaming."

"Concha," pages 255–258
"The Southpaw," pages 259–261
Recommended roles: Guide, Theme Master, Connector, Word Master
Also suggested: Genre Master, Highlighter, Sketcher, Investigator
Writing Prompt: "Do you think boys and girls should play together on sports teams? Why or why not?"

"Alexander the Great King," pages 269–278
Recommended roles: Guide, Genre Master, Highlighter, Geographer
Also suggested: Sketcher, Connector, Word Master, Investigator
Writing Prompt: "What do you think Alexander might have accomplished if he had lived about five more years?"

"A Backwoods Boy," pages 285–294
Recommended roles: Guide, Genre Master, Highlighter, Geographer
Also suggested: Sketcher, Connector, Word Master, Investigator
Writing Prompt: "What event from his early life do you think best prepared Abraham Lincoln for becoming president of the United States?"

Theme 4: What's Most Important

"The Stone," pages 311–318
Recommended roles: Guide, Genre Master, Theme Master, Highlighter
Also suggested: Sketcher, Connector, Word Master, Librarian
Writing Prompt: "Should everyone get one wish that will be granted? Why or why not?"

"April Rain Song," page 325
"In Just–," page 326
Recommended roles: Guide, Word Master, Poetry Master for Types of Poetry, Poetry Master for Repetition
Also suggested: Genre Master, Theme Master, Sketcher, Connector
Writing Prompt: "Do you like to read poetry with made-up words in it? Why?"

"Wings," pages 331–337
Recommended roles: Guide, Genre Master, Highlighter, Geographer
Also suggested: Theme Master, Sketcher, Connector, Word Master
Writing Prompt: "Was Daedalus too clever for his own good? Explain."

"The Flying Machine," pages 341–345
Recommended roles: Guide, Theme Master, Sketcher, Word Master
Also suggested: Genre Master, Highlighter, Connector, Geographer
Writing Prompt: "Which inventions would the world be better off without? Why?"

"The White Umbrella," pages 355–364
Recommended roles: Guide, Theme Master, Highlighter, Connector
Also suggested: Genre Master, Sketcher, Word Master, Librarian
Writing Prompt: "Do you think Americans want too many things, too many possessions?"

"Becky and the Wheels-and-Brake Boys," pages 371–377
Recommended roles: Guide, Theme Master, Connector, Word Master
Also suggested: Genre Master, Highlighter, Sketcher, Librarian
Writing Prompt: "Was Becky wrong to want a bike? Why?"

"President Cleveland, Where Are You?," pages 383–392
Recommended roles: Guide, Theme Master, Highlighter, Connector
Also suggested: Genre Master, Sketcher, Word Master, Investigator
Writing Prompt: "Are people always rewarded for doing the right thing? Explain."

Theme 5: The Will to Win

"Satchel Paige," pages 409–415
Recommended roles: Guide, Theme Master, Genre Master, Connector
Also suggested: Highlighter, Sketcher, Investigator, Geographer
Writing Prompt: "What do you think gives someone the will to win or to succeed?"

"The King of Mazy May," pages 422–431
Recommended roles: Guide, Theme Master, Highlighter, Geographer
Also suggested: Genre Master, Sketcher, Connector, Investigator
Writing Prompt: "Do you think the men in the story, including Walt Masters, were justified in the ways they tried to gain ownership of the claim? Explain."

"Priscilla and the Wimps," pages 435–438
Recommended roles: Guide, Highlighter, Sketcher, Connector
Also suggested: Theme Master, Genre Master, Word Master, Librarian
Writing Prompt: "What would you do if Monk 'ruled' your school?"

"Pecos Bill," pages 447–455
Recommended roles: Guide, Genre Master, Highlighter, Sketcher
Also suggested: Theme Master, Connector, Word Master, Geographer
Writing Prompt: "What might scare Pecos Bill? Explain."

"Baker's Bluejay Yarn," pages 463–467
Recommended roles: Guide, Genre Master, Sketcher, Word Master
Also suggested: Theme Master, Highlighter, Connector, Investigator
Writing Prompt: "What kinds of hopeless, misguided tasks do people try to accomplish, just as the blue jay did?"

"Doc Rabbit, Bruh Fox, and Tar Baby," page 473–476
"The Toad and the Donkey," pages 477–478
Recommended roles: Guide, Genre Master, Connector, Word Master
Also suggested: Theme Master, Highlighter, Sketcher, Librarian
Writing Prompt: "Is a folktale a good way to teach a lesson? Why?"

Theme 6: Getting Through Hard Times

"Whatif," page 495
"Life Doesn't Frighten Me," page 496
Recommended roles: Guide, Theme Master, Connector, Poetry Master for Repetition
Also suggested: Genre Master, Sketcher, Word Master, Poetry Master for Rhyming Patterns
Writing Prompt: "Is everyone frightened of something? Explain."

"Abd al-Rahman Ibrahima," pages 501–509
Recommended roles: Guide, Theme Master, Connector, Geographer
Also suggested: Genre Master, Highlighter, Sketcher, Investigator
Writing Prompt: "Do you think Ibrahima should have been released because he was the son of a chief? Explain."

"The Gold Cadillac," pages 515–525
Recommended roles: Guide, Theme Master, Highlighter, Connector
Also suggested: Genre Master, Sketcher, Geographer, Summarizer (if the selection is divided into two reading assignments)
Writing Prompt: "Describe a time when getting something you really wanted turned out differently than you expected."

"The Horse Snake," pages 531–535
Recommended roles: Guide, Genre Master, Highlighter, Sketcher
Also suggested: Theme Master, Connector, Investigator, Geographer
Writing Prompt: "Do you think this selection is nonfiction or a folktale? Explain."

From *Woodsong,* pages 539–541
Recommended roles: Guide, Theme Master, Highlighter, Sketcher
Also suggested: Genre Master, Connector, Word Master, Geographer
Writing Prompt: "What kind of 'conversation' do you think might have taken place among the dogs before they went back for the author?"

"The Dog of Pompeii," pages 546–554
Recommended roles: Guide, Genre Master, Highlighter, Sketcher
Also suggested: Theme Master, Connector, Investigator, Geographer
Writing Prompt: "Do you think the dog Bimbo ever existed? Explain."

from *Volcano,* pages 565–572
Recommended roles: Guide, Genre Master, Sketcher, Word Master
Also suggested: Theme Master, Highlighter, Investigator, Geographer
Writing Prompt: "Why do you think people are often caught by surprise when a volcano erupts?"

from *When Plague Strikes,* pages 579–589
Recommended roles: Guide, Genre Master, Theme Master, Word Master
Also suggested: Highlighter, Investigator, Geographer, Summarizer (if selection is divided into two reading assignments)
Writing Prompt: "If a disease that seemed to be highly contagious were spreading through your community, how might you react?"

Theme 7: Old Tales, New Twists

"Creation," pages 607–609
"Leyenda," page 610
Recommended roles: Guide, Genre Master for Folktale, Sketcher, Poetry Master for Types of Poetry
Also suggested: Theme Master, Connector, Word Master, Librarian
Writing Prompt: "Do you think groups of people somewhere on earth are writing new creation stories? Are all the creation stories already written? Explain."

"All Stories Are Anansi's," pages 615–618
"The End of the World," pages 619–620
Recommended roles: Guide, Genre Master, Sketcher, Word Master
Also suggested: Theme Master, Highlighter, Connector, Librarian
Writing Prompt: "Would you like to know if and when the world will end? Why?"

"Porcupine and the Sky Mirrors," pages 625–629
"The Fly," pages 630–632
Recommended roles: Guide, Genre Master, Highlighter, Sketcher
Also suggested: Theme Master, Connector, Word Master, Geographer
Writing Prompt: "How would The Fly differ if it were told from the viewpoint of the rich man? How would Porcupine and the Sky Mirrors be different if told by the Earth King?"

"Dragon, Dragon," pages 640–647
Recommended roles: Guide, Genre Master, Theme Master, Highlighter
Also suggested: Sketcher, Connector, Word Master, Librarian
Writing Prompt: "Would you rather read a story about a dragon that was scary? Why?"

"The Enchanted Raisin," pages 651–658
Recommended roles: Guide, Genre Master, Sketcher, Word Master
Also suggested: Theme Master, Highlighter, Connector, Investigator
Writing Prompt: "What do you think is the lesson contained in this story?"

Damon and Pythias, pages 668–675
Recommended roles: Guide, Genre Master, Highlighter, Connector
Also suggested: Theme Master, Sketcher, Word Master, Geographer
Writing Prompt: "Do you think there are friends today who are as loyal to each other as Damon and Pythias? Explain."

Theme 8: To Strange Places

"The Pied Piper of Hamelin," pages 693–703
Recommended roles: Guide, Genre Master, Highlighter, Poetry Master for Types of Poetry,
Also suggested: Theme Master, Connector, Investigator, Summarizer
Writing Prompt: "What advice would you give to the mayor of Hamelin? To the Pied Piper?"

"The Walrus and the Carpenter," pages 707–710
Recommended roles: Guide, Genre Master, Word Master, Poetry Master for Rhyming Patterns
Also suggested: Theme Master, Sketcher, Connector, Investigator
Writing Prompt: "Do you think the oysters deserve their fate? Why?"

"Aunt Millicent," pages 715–728
Recommended roles: Guide, Theme Master, Highlighter, Geographer
Also suggested: Genre Master, Connector, Word Master, Summarizer
Writing Prompt: "Explain whether you would have believed that Aunt Millicent was real, if you had been in Jamie's class."

Charlie and the Chocolate Factory, pages 735–764
Recommended roles: Guide, Genre Master, Connector, Summarizer
Also suggested: Theme Master, Highlighter, Sketcher, Word Master
Writing Prompt: "Would you like to tour the chocolate factory? Why or why not?"

"Future Tense," pages 771–780
Recommended roles: Guide, Genre Master, Theme Master, Highlighter
Also suggested: Sketcher, Connector, Word Master, Investigator
Writing Prompt: "What questions would you like to ask Dr. Proctor?"

"The Sand Castle," pages 787–791
Recommended roles: Guide, Genre Master, Highlighter, Connector
Also suggested: Theme Master, Sketcher, Word Master, Investigator
Writing Prompt: "In the story, the sun has become a dangerous force. Describe something else that was once believed to be helpful but now is hurting our environment."